Module 2 • Set 4 • Rabbits and Hares, Oh My!

CONTENTS

This book belongs to

. . . .

Great Minds® is the creator of *Eureka Math®*, *Wit & Wisdom®*, *Alexandria Plan™*, and *PhD Science®*.

Geodes® are published by Great Minds PBC in association with Wilson Language Training, publisher of Fundations®.

Credits

- *Rabbit or Hare?*: front cover (right) and p. 12, Bernd Wolter/Shutterstock.com; front cover (left) and p. 13, Jenny Cottingham/Shutterstock.com; p. ii (top), Jakub Mrocek/Shutterstock.com, (bottom), Masalski Maksim/Shutterstock.com; p. 2, Ger Bosma Photos/Shutterstock.com; p. 3, Arterra Picture Library/Alamy Stock Photo; p. 10, Arterra Picture Library/Alamy Stock Photo; p. 11, Andrew Paslavskiy/Shutterstock.com; More page (left), reptiles4all/Shutterstock.com, (right), defpicture/Shutterstock.com

- *Draw a Rabbit*: pp. 12–13, "Bunny" by Cate Bowman, "Hopping Bunny" by Annie Buonodono, "Two Furry Bunnies" by Mila Milner, "Bunnies" by Clara Newman, "Bunny Boing Boing" by Helaina Parsons; p. 14, "African Thorny Devil" by Rebecca Herpin, "The Bee" by Elise Howell, "Thorny Devil" by George Six, "Bumble Bee" by Sophia Six

- *The Hares and the Frogs*: folio icon, elisabetaaa/Shutterstock.com; More page, Lebrecht Music and Arts Photo Library/Alamy Stock Photo

- *Young Hare*: front and back covers and pp. i, 4, 7, 9, 11–13, The Albertina Museum, Vienna; p. ii, Public domain via Wikimedia Commons; p. 3, Jakub Mrocek/Shutterstock.com; p. 5, (top), Kate Moskvina/Shutterstock.com, (top two brushes), Bangkokhappiness/Shutterstock.com, (bottom brush), Sony Ho/Shutterstock.com; p. 6, (top left), 1989studio/Shutterstock.com, (middle and bottom left), Sergio Delle Vedove/Shutterstock.com, (middle), Sharon Kingston/Shutterstock.com, (right), Kate Moskvina/Shutterstock.com; p. 13 (right), Chris.R/Shutterstock.com; p. 14, (left), digital image courtesy of the Getty's Open Content Program, (right), The Albertina Museum, Vienna; More page, courtesy National Gallery of Art, Washington, DC

greatminds.org

ISBN 978-1-64497-423-0

Printed in the USA

2 3 4 5 6 7 8 9 10 LSC 26 25 24 23 22 21

Rabbit or Hare?

by Mamie Goodson 🐰 drawings by Rebecca Trahan

 I am a hare.

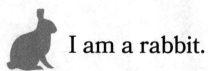 I am a rabbit.

We are a lot alike.

We have soft fur
and long ears.

Strong legs help us hop.

 Some think

we are the same.

 But we are not!

 I have long ears
with black tips.
My back legs
and feet are long.

I am smaller.
My ears and legs
are not as long.

4

 My long legs help me
run very fast.

 I can dash
here and there.
But I am not as fast.

5

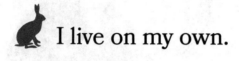 I live on my own.

I live in a group.

I fix my bed
on the land.

Some of us
dig dens.
Some of us
make nests.

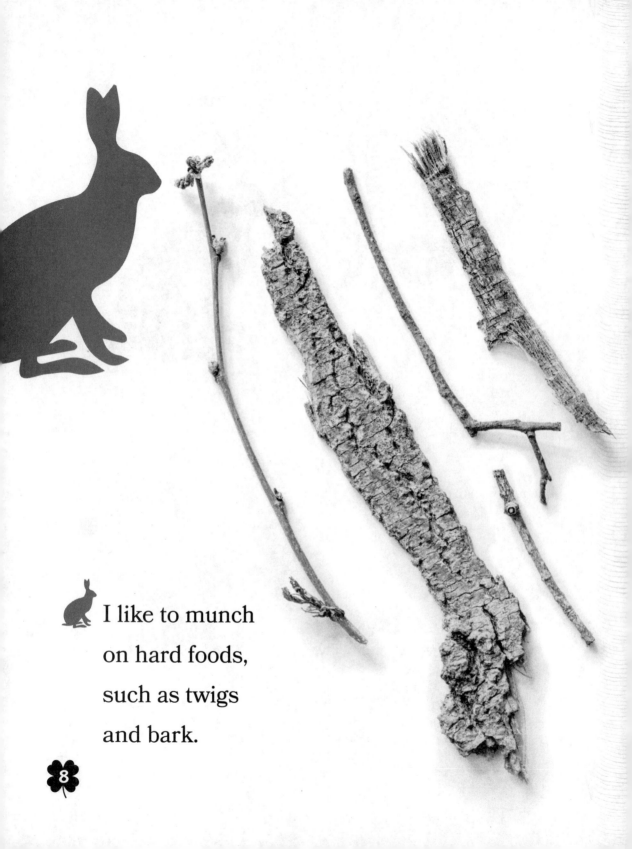

I like to munch
on hard foods,
such as twigs
and bark.

 I like soft foods,

such as grass,

buds,

and stems.

9

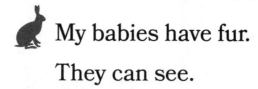 My babies have fur.
They can see.

 My kits do not have fur.
They do not see yet.

They can hop
and find food.

I must tend to my kits
for weeks.

We are a lot alike.

But we are not the same.

When you next spot
one of us,
observe us.
Can you tell
who is who?

13

About the Animals

A female hare is a jill.

A male hare is a jack.

Young hares are leverets.

A female rabbit is a doe.

A male rabbit is a buck.

Young rabbits are kits.

More

Like hares and rabbits, alligators and crocodiles are hard to tell apart. These reptiles both have a powerful bite, but their other features are more distinct.

Their appearances have some key differences. Alligators tend to be darker gray or blackish. Crocodiles are light tan or greenish. The snout, or nose, of an alligator is U-shaped. The snout of a crocodile looks more like a V.

Alligators and crocodiles also prefer different habitats. Alligators live in freshwater areas. Crocodiles are usually found in saltwater. South Florida is the only place in the world that is home to both animals.

Más

Es difícil distinguir a un caimán de un cocodrilo, así como es difícil distinguir a una liebre de un conejo. Ambos reptiles tienen una mordida poderosa, pero tienen otras características que los distinguen mejor.

Existen algunas diferencias fundamentales en su apariencia. Los caimanes tienden a ser negruzcos o gris oscuro. Los cocodrilos son de un tono claro o verdoso. El hocico, o nariz, de un caimán tiene forma de U, mientras que el del cocodrilo se parece más a una V.

Los caimanes y los cocodrilos también prefieren hábitats diferentes. Los caimanes viven en áreas de agua dulce. Los cocodrilos suelen encontrarse en agua salada. El sur de la Florida es el único lugar en el mundo donde habitan ambos animales.

Draw a Rabbit

text by
Catherine Schmidt

drawings by
Nicole Williams

photography by
Jimena Peck

It is a lot of fun to draw.

Things can come to life
with just a pencil
and some paper.

Let's draw a rabbit!
Set up your pad.

Step 1: The Head

Draw a ball.
It should not be
too big or too small.

Step 2: The Body

Next, put the tip of your pencil
on the side of the ball.
Bend a line down and around.
It ends up back on the ball.

Add 4
small lines.

Link them to
draw two legs.

Next, put two tall arcs on top.

Then, tuck a small arc in each one.

Step 5: The Eyes and Nose

Draw long dots for the eyes.

For the nose, add a

small line that bends up.

Step 6: The Mouth

From the nose, add a line that runs down.

At the tip of it, put a line with the ends bent up.

This is the mouth.

Add long thin lines for whiskers.

Add small lines at the tips for toes.

The rest
is up to you.

You could draw
two small rabbits.

You could
try a big
soft one.

9

You could
color one
black.

You could put one
in the grass.

11

It can be tricky to draw.

If you do it a lot, you will get better.

Bunny
Boing
Boing

13

You will bring lots of things to life
with just your pencil and a pad!

More

Artists combine color, form, line, shape, space, texture, and value to show their ideas visually. These seven elements are the building blocks of art.

Artists use these elements to draw. They start with simple shapes and lines and call this sketch an underdrawing. Their circles, ovals, triangles, and other shapes create the basic structure. Artists then add color, shading, texture, background, and more. Details bring their artwork to life.

Más

Los artistas combinan color, forma, línea, figura, espacio, textura y valor para expresar sus ideas en forma visual. Estos siete elementos son los componentes fundamentales del arte.

Los artistas usan estos elementos para dibujar. Comienzan con líneas y figuras simples. A este boceto le llaman dibujo preliminar. Sus círculos, óvalos, triángulos y otras figuras crean la estructura básica. Los artistas luego agregan color, sombreado, textura, fondo y otros elementos. Los detalles dan vida a sus obras.

THE HARES
AND THE FROGS

**RETOLD BY
MICHELLE PALMIERI**

**PICTURES BY
GIULIANO FERRI**

One day,
the hares
went up the big hill.

"I think it's time for lunch,"
one said.

They set off
to find grass and twigs.

Hares, as you know,

are full of fear.

So, as they had lunch,

they kept alert.

It was not long

before one hare

sat up in a rush.

Sniff, sniff.

An animal was close by.

"Run!" the hare yelled.
And off they ran,
as fast as they could.

But it was just a sheep.

The hares felt bad
for running off.
They went over
to the shrubs
to rest.

6

When some twigs went
SNAP,
they got up in a flash,
and fled.

But it was just the ducks.

The big hare said,

"We are a sad bunch.

We let fear rob us

of food and rest."

"Let us find a spot to hide.

We may not have grass there,

but we will be safe.

We will not be afraid."

With that,

the hares set off.

On the path

there was a pond.

A group of frogs

sat by the bank.

As the hares went by,

the frogs went into the pond.

Plop! Plop!

They hid.

"Look!" said a hare.

"Did you see the frogs jump?

Things are not so bad

after all."

"We are not the only ones
who are afraid.
Even the frogs ran and hid . . .
from us!"

13

We all have fears to face.

MORE

A fable is a short story that teaches a moral, or lesson. Aesop's fables have been retold for thousands of years and continue to teach and entertain. Aesop's name has been linked to hundreds of fables.

Although the hares in this fable are fictional, in some ways they behave like the real animals. Hares are usually solitary, but they may forage, or look for food, in groups. While they forage, the group watches for predators. If a predator gets too close, hares use their strong legs to run away. They can reach top speeds of up to 45 miles per hour.

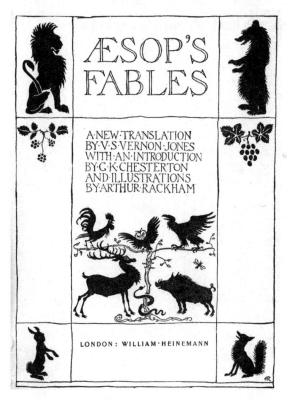

Aesop's Fables, frontispiece. 1933 edition translated by V. S. Vernon Jones, illustrated by Arthur Rackham, London: William-Heinemann.

MÁS

Una fábula es un cuento corto que presenta una moraleja, o enseñanza. Las fábulas de Esopo se han relatado durante miles de años y siguen entreteniendo y dejando enseñanzas. El nombre de Esopo se ha vinculado a cientos de fábulas.

Si bien las liebres de esta fábula son personajes de ficción, se comportan, de alguna manera, como animales de verdad. Las liebres suelen ser solitarias, pero pueden buscar alimentos en grupos. Mientras buscan alimentos, el grupo está atento a los depredadores. Si uno se acerca demasiado, las liebres usan sus fuertes patas para huir. Pueden alcanzar velocidades máximas de hasta 45 millas por hora.

1503

ART and
ARTISTS

Young Hare

BY MICHELLE PALMIERI

Albrecht Dürer, *Columbine*, 1526, watercolor and gouache on parchment, heightened with white, 14 x 11 inches, Albertina Museum, Vienna, Austria.

Long ago,
there was a man.
This man could find art
in many things.

He saw art in the land
and in the grass.

Where some would see just a small hare,
this artist saw wonder.

What do you see?

A hare is soft

with fur and fluff.

Dürer painted this to look real—

as if it could jump

into your lap!

Albrecht Dürer, *Young Hare*, 1502, watercolor and gouache, 10 x 9 inches, Albertina Museum, Vienna, Austria.

How did he do it?

Back then, he had

watercolors,

a thick brush,

a thin brush,

and a very thin brush.

We can look at colors and lines
to see how he did it.

Dürer painted with colors
that best fit a real hare.

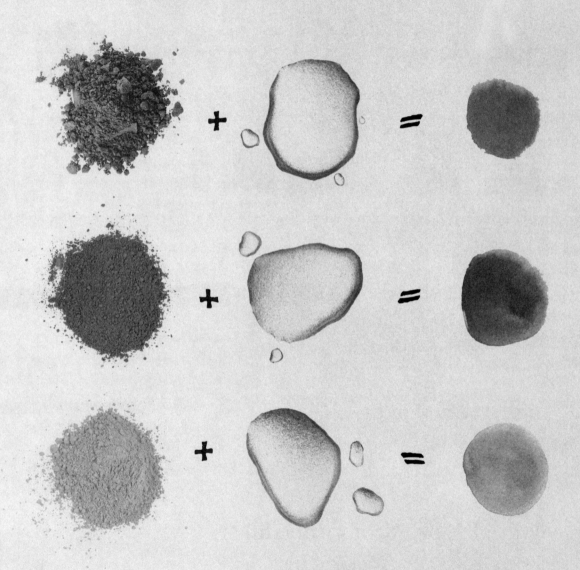

What colors do you see? 1502

7

He put big dabs of color on
with a thick brush.

He put small lines on top
with a thin brush.

He put tiny lines here and there
with a very thin brush.

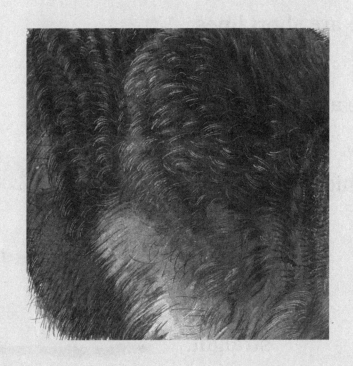

Which colors are on top?

Dürer painted lots of lines.

There are long lines.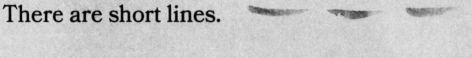
There are short lines.

There are

    thick,

    thin,
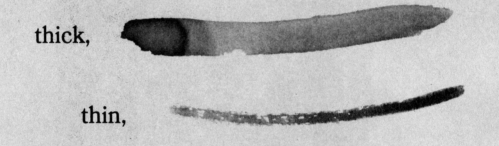

    straight,

    and curved lines.

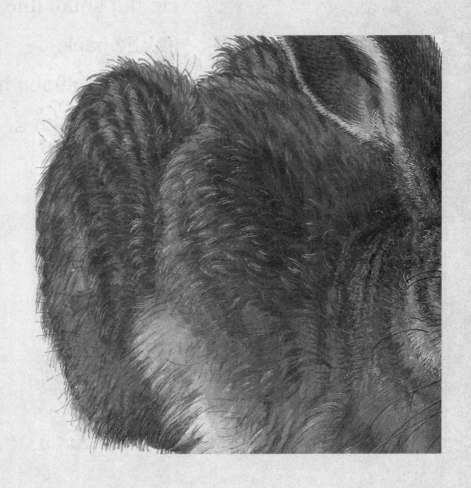

What kinds of lines do you see?

11

He put small lines
on the back.
He painted long lines
for the whiskers.

12

1502

Just as he did with color,
he put thin lines on top of thick ones.

This helps the fur look
soft and thick.

The mix of lines
makes the hare look real.
The colors help, too.

Where some saw just a hare,

Dürer saw much, much more.

He saw art in small things,

in *all* things.

Albrecht Dürer, *Stag Beetle*, 1505, watercolor and gouache, 5 ½ x 4 ½ inches, J. Paul Getty Museum, Los Angeles, United States.

Albrecht Dürer, *Wing of a Blue Roller*, 1512, watercolor and gouache, 7 ¾ x 8 inches, Albertina Museum, Vienna, Austria.

Where do you see art?

More

Albrecht Dürer is an important Renaissance artist. He created watercolor and pencil sketches. He is also known for his oil paintings, engravings, and woodcut prints.

One of Dürer's well-known woodcuts depicts a rhinoceros. Usually, Dürer drew animals by carefully studying the world around him. For this print, however, he did not have a real animal to observe. Instead, he relied on the descriptions and sketches of others. Dürer's rhinoceros has an extra horn, armor-like skin, and scaly legs. Although the depiction was not accurate, it fascinated viewers.

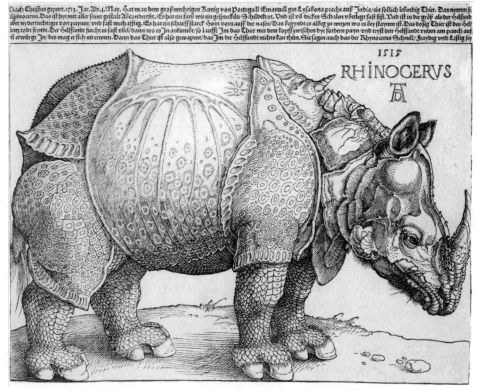

Albrecht Dürer, *The Rhinoceros*, 1515, woodcut, 9 ¼ x 11 ¾ inches, National Gallery of Art, Washington, DC, United States.

Más

Albrecht Dürer es un artista importante del Renacimiento. Pintaba acuarelas y hacía dibujos a lápiz. También es conocido por sus pinturas al óleo, grabados y xilografías.

Una de las xilografías más conocidas de Dürer representa un rinoceronte. Generalmente, Dürer dibujaba animales luego de analizar cuidadosamente el mundo que lo rodeaba. Sin embargo, para hacer este grabado no podía observar el animal directamente. Entonces, tuvo que basarse en las descripciones y los dibujos de otras personas. El rinoceronte de Dürer tiene un cuerno adicional, la piel igual a una armadura y patas escamosas. A pesar de que la representación no es exacta, causó fascinación entre aquellos que la vieron.